Gus Can Get a Pet

by Liza Charlesworth

ISBN: 978-1-338-84427-6

Art Director: Tannaz Fassihi; Designer: Cynthia Ng; Illustrated by Kevin Zimmer
Copyright © Liza Charlesworth. All rights reserved. Published by Scholastic Inc.

3 4 5 6 7   68   26 25 24

Printed in Jiaxing, China. First printing, June 2022.

SCHOLASTIC

"Can I get a pet?" said Gus.
"Yes!" said his dad.

Gus and his dad went on a jog.
"It is a fox!" said Gus.

"Can I get a fox?" said Gus.
"A fox is not a pet," said his dad.

Jog, jog, jog.
"It is a bat!" said Gus.

"Can I get a bat?" said Gus.
"A bat is not a pet," said his dad.

Jog, jog, jog.
"It is a bug!" said Gus.

"Can I get a bug?" said Gus.
"A bug is not a pet," said his dad.

Jog, jog, jog.
"It is a cap!" said Gus.

"I can hop!" it said.
Hop, hop, hop.

"I can sit!" it said.
Sit, sit, sit.

"Can I get a cap?" said Gus.
"Yes!" said his dad.
"A cap IS a pet."

"Can I put it on?" said Gus.
"Yes!" said his dad.

Pat, pat, pat.
"A cap is a fab pet!" said Gus.
"Yes, I am!" it said.

Read & Review

Invite your learner to point to each short-vowel word and read it aloud.

Short a pat

am can cap fab

dad bat

Short e

pet yes

get

Short i

is   it   sit   his

Short u

bug
Gus

Short o

jog   fox   on   not   hop

Fun Fill-Ins

Read the sentences aloud, inviting your learner to complete them using the short-vowel words in the box.

> pet   Gus   jog   sit   cap

1. This story is about a dad and his son, _____.

2. Dad and Gus went on a _____.

3. Dad said, "A bat is not a _____."

4. Gus saw a cap hop and _____.

5. At the end, Gus's dad let him get a pet _____.